Grade 1

The Syllabus of Examinations should be read for details of requirements, especially those for scales, aural tests and sight-reading. Attention should be paid to the Special Notices on the front inside cover, where warning is given of changes.

The syllabus is obtainable from music dealers or from The Associated Board of the Royal Schools of Music, 14 Bedford Square, London WC1B 3JG (please send a stamped addressed envelope measuring about 9 × 6 ins.).

In overseas centres, information may be obtained from the Local Representative or Resident Secretary.

Requirements

SCALES, ARPEGGIOS AND BROKEN CHORDS
(from memory)

Scales
(i) each hand separately, up and down
(or down and up in L.H. at candidate's choice)
in the following keys:
C, G, D, F majors and A, D minors
(melodic or harmonic minor at candidate's choice)
(all two octaves)
(ii) in contrary motion, both hands beginning and ending on the key-note (unison), in the key of C major only (one octave)

Arpeggios
the common chords of C, G and F majors, and A and D minors, in root position only, each hand separately (one octave)

Broken Chords
formed from the chords of C, G and F majors, and A and D minors, each hand separately, according to the pattern shown in the syllabus

PLAYING AT SIGHT (see current syllabus)

AURAL TESTS (see current syllabus)

THREE PIECES

LIST A   page
1 **Félix Le Couppey** (1811-1887)
   Melody in C   3
2 **Daniel Gottlob Türk** (1750-1813)
   There it goes at full gallop   4
3 **Richard Rodney Bennett**
   Monday, from 'Seven Days a Week'   5

LIST B
1 **Henry Purcell** (1659-1695)
   Air in D minor, Z.T676   6
2 **James Hook** (1746-1827)
   Gavotta in C, Op.81, Lesson 3   7
3 **Béla Bartók** (1881-1945)
   Quasi Adagio, No.3 from 'For Children', Vol. I   8

Candidates must prepare Nos.1 & 2 from the *same* list, A *or* B, but may choose No.3 from *either* list *or* one of the further alternatives listed below:

C. Gurlitt   Waltz in F, Op.179 No.21
F. Wohlfahrt   Allegretto
These are included in More Romantic Pieces for Piano, Book I, *published by the Associated Board*

A:1
MELODY in C

LE COUPPEY

Moderato [♩ = c.96]

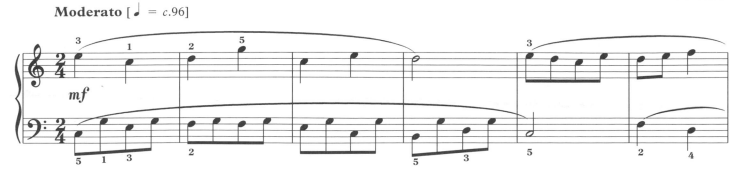

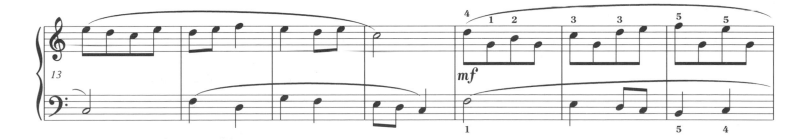

Le Couppey was Professor of Piano at the Paris Conservatoire and wrote many sets of studies and instructional pieces for the piano, including *ABC du piano* (1859), from which this piece is taken. Dynamics and phrasing are editorial suggestions only.

A:2
THERE IT GOES AT FULL GALLOP

TÜRK

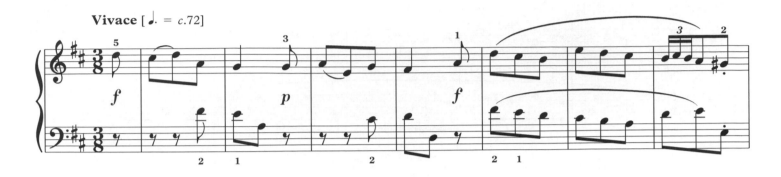

Türk composed two sets of *Handstücke für angehende Klavierspieler* (1792, 1795); this piece is from the second set. All dynamics (except for the initial *f*) are Türk's, as are all two-note slurs; other marks of articulation are editorial suggestions only. Cadential ornaments have been written out.

Both sets of Türk's *Handstücke* are available under the title, *Sixty Pieces for Aspiring Players*, Books I and II, edited by Howard Ferguson and published by the Associated Board.

A:3
MONDAY
from 'Seven Days a Week'

RICHARD RODNEY BENNETT

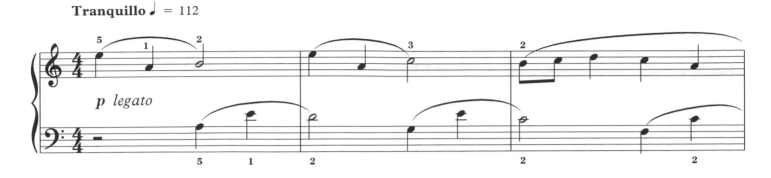

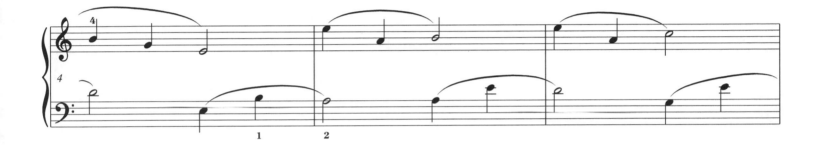

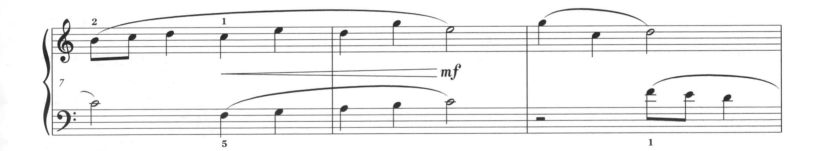

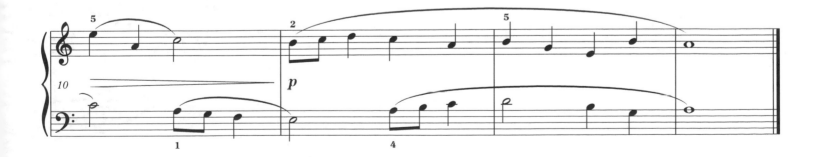

B:1
AIR in D minor

PURCELL, Z.T676

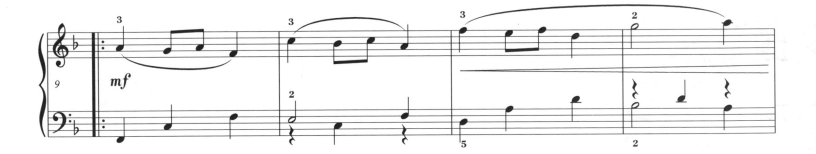

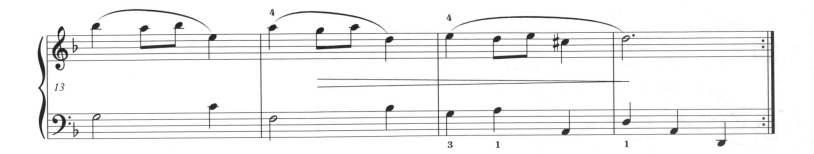

This is a transcription of a Minuet for strings from Purcell's incidental music to Congreve's comedy, *The Double Dealer*. The left-hand part has been adapted slightly to take out octave stretches. Dynamics and phrase-marks are editorial suggestions only.

B:2
GAVOTTA in C

JAMES HOOK, Op.81, Lesson 3

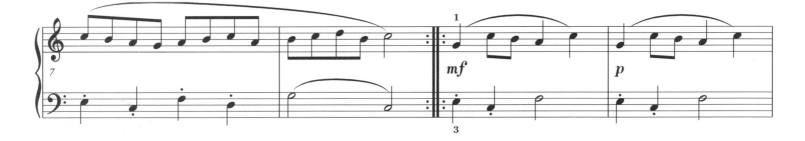

James Hook showed his musical gifts at an early age, playing the harpsichord at the age of four and performing in public at six. He was also a renowned piano teacher and this piece is from a collection of his teaching pieces, *New Guida di Musica* (1796). All dynamics and marks of articulation are editorial suggestions only and players may wish to consider alternatives appropriate to the style.

B:3
QUASI ADAGIO
No.3 from 'For Children', Vol.I

BARTÓK